LADY IN THE DARK

Musical Play

By

MOSS HART

Lyrics by   *Music by*

IRA GERSHWIN   KURT WEILL

VOCAL SCORE

(Edited by Albert Sirmay)

CHAPPELL & CO., INC.

RKO Building ● Rockefeller Center
New York, N. Y.

LADY IN THE DARK

Was Presented By

SAM H. HARRIS

with

GERTRUDE LAWRENCE

at the Alvin Theatre, New York, on January 23rd, 1941

Cast of Characters

DR. BROOKS....................................DONALD RANDOLPH

MISS BOWERS..................................JEANNE SHELBY

LIZA ELLIOTT..............................GERTRUDE LAWRENCE

MISS FOSTER................................EVELYN WYCKOFF

MISS STEVENS.....................................ANN LEE

MAGGIE GRANT..............................MARGARET DALE

ALISON DU BOIS............................NATALIE SCHAFER

RUSSELL PAXTON................................DANNY KAYE

CHARLEY JOHNSON......................MACDONALD CAREY

RANDY CURTIS..............................VICTOR MATURE

JOE, an office boy............................WARD TALLMON

TOM, an office boy.........................GEORGE BOCKMAN

KENDALL NESBITT..............................BERT LYTELL

HELEN, a model............................VIRGINIA PEINE

RUTHIE, a model.............................GEDDA PETRY

CAROL, a model..............................BETH NICHOLS

MARCIA, a model.......................MARGARET WESTBERG

BEN BUTLER.....................................DAN HARDEN

BARBARA....................................PATRICIA DEERING

JACK..DAVIS CUNNINGHAM

Musical Direction by Maurice Abravanel

PRODUCTION BY HASSARD SHORT

One rainy afternoon a year ago Kurt Weill and myself sat at a table in a little midtown restaurant and told each other vehemently why we would not write a musical comedy. Kurt Weill because he would not write the music for the regulation musical comedy book, and myself because I would not write the book for the regulation musical comedy music.

We parted in complete agreement though it was a far cry from the purpose of the meeting. We had arranged to meet to see if we could not do a show together and had thoroughly succeeded in discovering that we couldn't. That is, we were both completely disinterested in doing a show for the sake of doing a show, in Broadway parlance, and the tight little formula of the musical comedy stage held no interest for either of us.

We met again the following week and after another luncheon, that lasted well into the evening, we discovered the kind of show we both definitely *did* want to do.

It was, we decided, a show in which the music carried forward the essential story and was not imposed on the architecture of the play as a rather melodious but useless addenda.

This is an easy phrase to write but to achieve that end it was necessary to create both a new technique and a new musical form. I say this at the risk of sounding a little pompous, but it seems to me that in "Lady in the Dark" this has in some measure been successfully accomplished.

I cannot in all modesty discuss my own contribution, but I can with enormous enthusiasm discuss the contributions of Kurt Weill and Ira Gershwin. They have, it seems to me, created a new musical and lyrical pattern in the American Theatre. I think for the first time—at least so far as my memory serves,—the music and lyrics of a musical "show" are part and parcel of the basic structure of the play. One cannot separate the play from the music or vice versa. More than that, the music and lyrics carry the story forward dramatically and psychologically.

All this, it seems to me, has been done with enormous resource, musicianship and skill. As a dramatist interested in new forms in the theatre it seems to me that Kurt Weill has made a contribution to our present day theatre of inestimable value.

MOSS HART

March 18, 1941

INDEX

LADY IN THE DARK

I. Glamour Dream

Words by
IRA GERSHWIN

Music by
KURT WEILL

Pink-er-ton, What Ca-lam-i-ty Jane was to Buf-fa-lo Bill, What Car-men was to Don Jo-

sé Are you to me _____ SIX MEN Oh, Fab-u-lous One in your i-vo-ry tower Oh,

Sweet, this is no pot-pour-ri. What Mel-i-sande was to Pel-le-as Are you to

Sweet, this is no pot-pour-ri What Mel-i-sande was to Pel-le-as Are you to

Andante amoroso (♩ = 100)

me.

me.

(Sutton, the maid, appears)

ƒ

Più mosso (♩ = 152)

SUTTON

I'm Miss Ell - iot's maid. Gen-tle-men, I'm a - fraid Your

p

leggiero

loy - al - ty we must be test - ing. She can-not be seen, she's rest - ing. But she

(free) *(a tempo)* MEN

wish-es to thank you all for the ser - e - nade. Give the la - dy a -

> > > *p*

C-1106-128 Lady In The Dark Score

bove Sal - u - ta - tions and love. Ad - vise her we leave in sweet

sor - row. But that we re-turn on the mor - row With our night-ly ser - e -

Allegro giocoso (♩.= 132)

(They march off)

nade._____ Each night we ser - e - nade the love-ly

la - dy we a - dore__ Who oc - cu - pies the sev - en-teenth to twen-ty - sec - ond

18

BEEKMAN

all oth - er wo - men ap - pear Ham-mach - er Schlam-mo - rous.

Allegro moderato (♩ = 132)

A thou-sand par-dons I must quit the scene I must be off to per-fume the gas-o-line.

(He dances off.)

Appassionato (♩ = 100)

(Liza enters)

a - ta. Sev - en thou-sand stu-dents say they look to you To

be at the Yale Har-vard Re - gat - ta. Ep - stein says you sim - ply have to

pose for him. Here's the key to the Is - land of To - ba - go.

Du Pont wants you wear-ing the new hose for him. Can you chris-ten a bat-tle-ship in San Di-

24

C-1106-128 The Lady In The Dark Score

Allegro moderato (♩.=52)

ra - ta

pp

p

LIZA
I'll probably   motor to Bear Mountain to see the sun rise.   You needn't wait up. Good night!

p   poco a poco rit.   dim.

SUTTON
Good night, Miss Elliott.   Allegro vivace *(fast waltz)* (♩.=72)

f a tempo   *(She waltzes)*

ff

(Beekman appears with the car)

mf

Allegro molto (♩=132)

BEEKMAN
I learned it would be blue tonight. So I'm driving the blue Dusenberg with the blue license plates and

I've put the blue Picasso in the car.

LIZA
Very thoughtful, Beekman.

BEEKMAN
Where to Miss Elliott?

LIZA
The "Seventh Heaven!"   Più mosso

cresc. poco a poco

(They drive in the car)

mf

Presto

f

LIZA
Where are we Beekman?

BEEKMAN
Columbus Circle.

LIZA
Would you get me my blue soapbox, please. I want to make a speech.

One Life To Live

Allegro animato (♩ = 144)

LIZA

There are man-y minds in cir-cu-la-tion, Be-liev-ing in re-in-car-na-tion. In me you see One who does-n't a - gree.

slower

Chal-leng-ing pos-si-ble af-fronts, I be-lieve I'll on-ly live

once And I want to make the most of it. If there's a

par-ty I want to be the host of it; If there's a haunt-ed house I want to be the

ghost of it; If I'm in town I want to be the toast of it.

poco rit.

(The Nightclub appears)
Andante non troppo (♩ = 84)

(In Nightclub)
Tempo di Fox-trot (♩ = 116)

36

moment to the heights no more you'll climb

MEN
My dreams are torn a-

sun- der Your im - age I

drew I see you now and

End of 1st Dream.

II. Wedding Dream

tell it now. On grad-u-a-tion day when Li - za de-liv-ered the Va-le-dic-to-ry I

asked her if she'd wait for me. She

smiled. She did-n't take me ser-ious-ly.

GIRL
I never quite understood her. She had a pretty voice though.

Allegro moderato (♩ = 100)

Soprano (*Mapleton Highschool song*)

Alto

We sing the praise of Ma-ple-ton High! Each heart is filled with loy-al-ty. And

Tenor

We sing the praise of Ma-ple-ton High! Each heart is filled with loy-al-ty. And

Bass

We sing the praise of Ma-ple-ton High! Each heart is filled with loy-al-ty. And

Allegro ma non troppo

BOY
She was a wiz at tennis; one time I had her 5 - 2
point set. She beat me 9 - 7.

ANOTHER BOY
Remember that caricature she drew of M. d'Albert

the French teacher? Instead of getting sore at her he took it home to show to his wife.

ALL (spoken)
Le - la - les!   Par-lez vous Fran-cais?   Ou-vrez la fe - nê - tre   sil vaus plait.

(dreamily)
La la la la la la   la la la la la   La la la la la la   La la la la la.

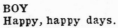

mar-ried.   Li - za   Ell-iott is mar-ry-ing   Ken-dall

(Kendall Nesbitt enters)   **ONE GIRL** *(spoken)*

Nes-bitt.   Ken-dall Nes - bitt is   for-ty-eight years old.   He   loves

Li - za and   Li - za loves him. They get a - long beau-ti-ful-ly

Soprano   *p*
Alto   It's   quite i -
Tenor   *p*   It's   quite i -
(Liza enters)   Bass   It's   quite i -

dyl-lic.   **ONE BOY** *(spoken)*

dyl-lic.   He start-ed the ma-ga-zine   for her.   It's been most   suc-

dyl-lic.

C-1106-128   Lady In The Dark Score

see him ev-'ry week   And for-ty mil-lion wom-en

Ran-dy   Cur-tis!

love him.   In   Kan-sas, in Pat-a-gon-ia,   in

Hol-ly-wood it-self   He is a man   ev-'ry wom-an

wants.

Andante cantabile (♩ = 56)   RANDY
Darling, at last!

(espr.)
p

This Is New

RANDY
(with warmth)

With you I used to roam Through the Pleas-ure Dome of Kub-la Khan,

I held you tight, my love, In the gar-dens of Old Bab-y-lon,

— I lost you through the cen-tur-ies. I find you once a-

gain, And find my-self the luck-i-est of men.

LIZA

I don't know.

ALL

What's wor-ry-ing you Li-za? What are you a-fraid of?

(sing)

You should be hap-py. Ev-'ry wom-an wants to be mar-ried And

mf

this is the eve of your wed-ding day.

ALL

What are you think-ing of?

dim.

LIZA

How curious. How very curious. Of all the things I could be thinking of at this moment, a little school play I acted in as a child keeps running through my mind.

p

LIZA
I was to have been the princess, but I wasn't._I don't remember why.

The Princess Of Pure Delight

tossed at night For the neigh-bor-ing Princess of pure de-light! *(spoken) Who was secretly in love with*

a minstrel! *(sung)* Her fa-ther, the King, did-n't know which to choose, There were

two charm-ing Princ-es he'd have to re-fuse So he called for the dean of his sor-cer-ers and In-

quired which one was to win her hand. *(spoken) Which they always did in those days.* *(sung)* My

Poco meno mosso

King here's a rid-dle, you test them to-night. 'What word of five let-ters is

nev-er spelled right, What word of five let-ters is al-ways spelled wrong?' The

one who can an-swer will be wed-ded ere long."(spoken)*That will be twenty gulden, please.*(sung)The

Allegretto grazioso (♩ = 104)

King called the three and he told them the test, The while his fair daugh-ter kept

beat-ing her breast. He put them the rid-dle. They failed as he feared. Then

Allegro giocoso (♩. = 88)

all of a sud-den the Min-strel ap-peared. *(spoken)* **Quite out of breath!** *(sung)* "I'll

an-swer that rid-dle" cried the sing-er of song, "What's nev-er spelled right in five let-ters is

'wrong'. And it's right to spell 'wrong' W - R-O-N-G. Your
(double U)

she can wed me." "By Gad" cried his high-ness, "You hand-some young knave, I

fear me you're right!" and his bless-ing he gave. *(spoken) As a trumpeter began to trumpet. (sung)* The

Moderato assai

Princ-ess then quick-ly came out of her swoon And she looked at her swain and her

world was in tune. And the cas-tle soon rang with cheer and with laugh - ter

C-1106-128   Lady In The Dark Score

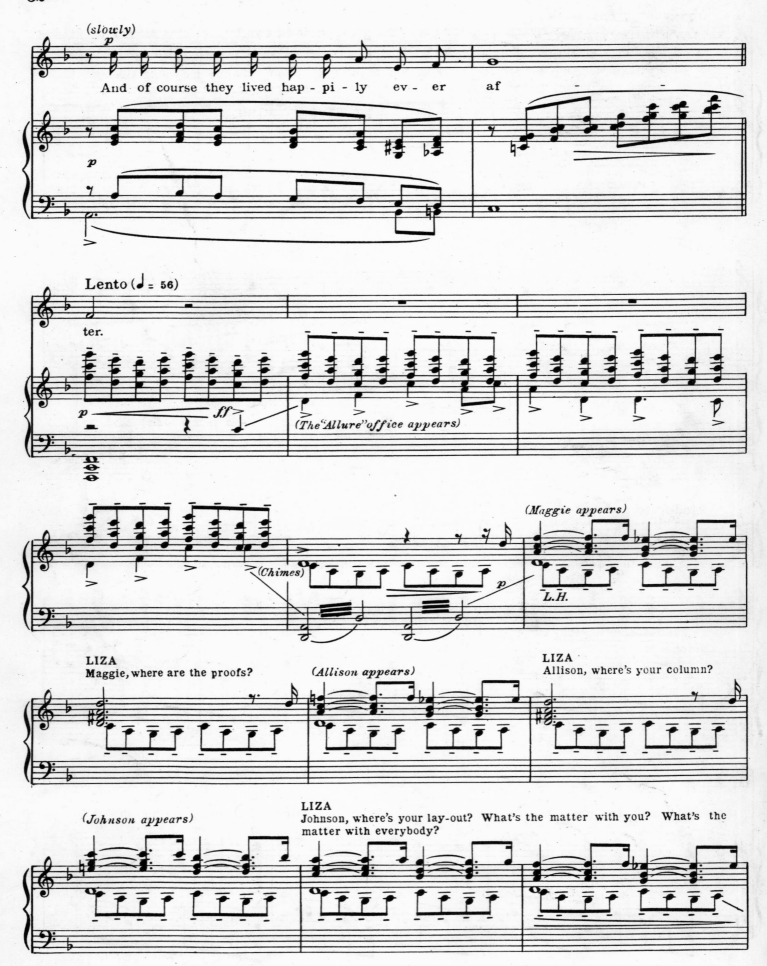

(slowly)

And of course they lived hap-pi-ly ev-er af- - - -ter.

Lento (♩ = 56)

(The "Allure" office appears)

(Maggie appears)

(Chimes)

L.H.

LIZA
Maggie, where are the proofs?

(Allison appears)

LIZA
Allison, where's your column?

(Johnson appears)

LIZA
Johnson, where's your lay-out? What's the matter with you? What's the matter with everybody?

JOHNSON
Why, don't you know what day this is, Boss Lady? This is your wedding day! Your wedding day! Your wedding

misterioso

day! *(He disappears)*

LIZA
Maggie! Allison! Speak to me!

What is this?

MAGGIE and ALLISON
It's late, Liza! It's late! You must hurry! This is your wedding day!

Maestoso

(The church appears)

CHARLIE *(In a louder tone)*
If there be any who know why these two should

trust they Loh- en- grin and bear it.

accel. *cresc.* *a tempo*

sf

not be joined in holy wedlock, let him speak now or forever hold his peace.

SEPULCHRAL VOICE

(Bass) The

pp

mur-mur-ings of con-science do in-crease   And con-science can no long-er hold its peace.   This

twain should ne'er be joined in ho-ly wed-lock   Or e'en in se-cu-lar board and bed-lock.

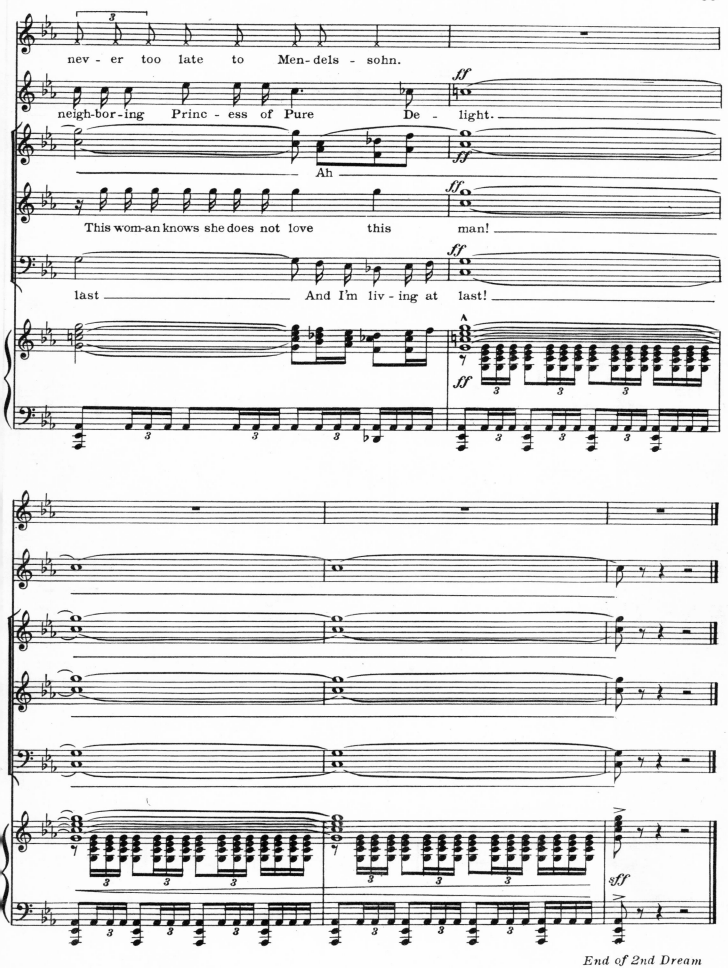

End of 2nd Dream

III. Circus Dream

tszing, ta - ra - ra,——— Ta - ra - ra tszing, tszing, tszing, ta - ra - ra,

tszing, tszing, tszing, ta - ra - ra, tszing, tszing, tszing, ta - ra - ra - ra!———

— The Great - est Show On Earth! It's Full Of Thrills and Mirth! You Get Your

Mon - ey's Worth! Come one come all!———————— Come see the Midg - ets and the

96

Mirth! The Great-est Show On Earth! Come one come all!

Mirth! The Great-est Show On Earth! Come one come all!

Mirth! The Great-est Show On Earth! Come one come all!

(The Ringmaster enters)

Moderato assai ($\quad$ = 80)

RINGMASTER

La-dies and Gen-tle-men, I Take Pride in In-tro-duc-ing The Great-est Show On

Stars of the Tan-bark Ring

And a Gal-ax-y Of Clowns and Neu - ro-ses

In a Mod-ern Mir-a-cle of Mel-o-dra-ma-tic Buf-foon - er-y

And Men-tal Tight Rope Walk - ing!

The Great-est Show On

Tempo I (♩ = 138)

Earth!

Soprano *f* ALL
Alto
The Flow'r Of Wom - an -
Tenor *f*
The Flow'r Of Wom - an -
Bass *f*
The Flow'r Of Wom - an -

Dance Of The Tumblers

Presto *(doppio movimento)*

C-1106-128   Lady In The Dark Score

RINGMASTER
Order in the courtroom!

PAGE
The charges against
Liza Elliott.
RINGMASTER
Thank you, my dear.

LIZA
What is all this? Charges against me? What for? What is all this?

Sostenuto (♩= 88)

RINGMASTER   (Free)

Where-as   Li-za El-li-ott can-not make up her mind a-bout the

Soprano

Alto
Where-as

Tenor
Where-as

Bass
Where-as

East-er cov-er or the cir-cus cov-er;   Se-cun-dus   Li-za

Se-cun-dus!

Se-cun-dus!

Se-cun-dus!

El-li-ott can-not make up her mind wheth-er she is mar-ry-ing Ken-dall Nes-bitt or not; More

o-ver   Li-za El-li-ott can-not make up her mind as to the kind of wom-an

More o-ver!

More o-ver!

More o-ver!

she wants to be, the ex-ec-u-tive or the en-chan-tress; And in as much as   In a

In as much as _

In as much as _

In as much as _

C-1106-128   Lady In The Dark Score

world where tu-mult and tur-moil reign, these in-de-ci-sions of Li - za El - li -ott on - ly add to the

con - fu-sions of an al - read - y, as in - di - ca - ted, con - fused world; There-fore,

be it re-solved That Li-za El-li-ott be brought to trial and be made to make up her mind.

Be it re-solved!

Be it re-solved!

Be it re-solved!

ff

ff

ff

mf

ff

Presto (♩ = 144)
(Cheer)

RINGMASTER
Introducing that death defying
trapeze artist and Prosecuting
Attorney, Charlie Johnson!

Allegro animato (♩. = 120)
(Charlie marches on)

(Drum)

CHARLIE

I'm the at - tor - ney for pro - se - cu - tion, Can't be bought or sold! For the

jam she's in there's no so - lu - tion, Once the sto - ry is told!

ALL

He's the at - tor - ney for pro - se - cu - tion Fly - ing in - to space!___

Will there be an e - lec - tro - cu - tion If he wins the case?

RINGMASTER
Introducing that thrilling bareback rider
and Attorney for the defence Randy Curtis! *(Randy marches on)*

RANDY
I'm the law - yer for the de - fend - ant, Can't be sold or bought! ___ Miss

El - li - ott's star is in the as - cend - ant; This will come to naught!

RINGMASTER
Introducing those merry madcaps and
prankish pantaloonatics, the Jury.

JURY

Our ob-ject all sub-

L'istesso tempo (♩ = 120)

ALL

Gil - bert and Sell - i - vant! Ha - ha - ha - ha - ha - ha - ha - ha - ha

f **L.H.**

ha! If this is just a sam - ple Then ev - i - dence is

sf

p leggiero

am - ple You get your mon - ey's worth At The Great - est Show On

CHARLIE
Your honor, Mr. Ringmaster, I would like to introduce
that peerless witness and lion tamer, Kendall Nesbitt.   *(Nesbitt enters)*

Earth.

ff   *f*

3

116

C-1106-128 Lady In The Dark Score

through! What a mess of a mish mash this is!

through! What a mess of a mish mash this is!

through! What a mess of a mish mash this is!

RANDY
Your Honor Mr. Ringmaster.

RINGMASTER
Yes, Mr. Bareback Rider.

RANDY
I would like to answer the charge just made by the prosecuting attorney.

RINGMASTER
Go ahead, I can hardly wait.

RANDY

She

Con sentimento

gave him her heart, but not her word— This case, there-fore,

a tempo

is so much dead - wood —— Her prom - ise to wed he

nev - er heard For she nev - er prom - ised she wed would..

—— It's just that a change of heart oc - curred And al - though it

may have dis - mayed him —— When a maid gives her heart but does not give her

120

C-1106-128 Lady In The Dark Score

122

Tschaikowsky

Allegro barbaro (♩ = 152)

(not too fast and well pronounced)

There's Ma-li-chev-sky, Ru-ben-stein, A - ren-sky and Tschai-

kow-sky, Sa - pel-ni-koff, Di-mit-ri-eff, Tsche-rep-nin, Kry-ja-now-sky, Go-dow-sky, Ar-tei-

bou-cheff, Mo-ni-usz-ko, A-ki-men-ko, So - lo-vi-eff, Pro-ko-fi-eff, Ti - om-kin, Ko-rest-

chen-ko. There's Glin-ka, Wink-ler, Bort-ni-an-sky, Re-bi-koff, Il-yin-sky, There's Medt-ner, Ba-la-

C-1106-128 Lady In The Dark Score

RINGMASTER
Proceed with the trial.
CHARLIE
Mr. Ringmaster, I would like to call Miss Liza Elliott.
RINGMASTER
And about time too.

RINGMASTER
Introducing that dazzling defendant and peerless proponent of mental acrobatics, Miss Liza Elliott.

Allegretto (♩ = 69)

CHARLIE
Miss Elliott, you've heard the charges against you. Have you made up your mind about any of these things?

Soprano
Alto
Tenor
Bass

And now the star at - trac-tion The Great-est in the Land! The
And now the star at - trac-tion The Great-est in the Land! The
And now the star at - trac-tion The Great-est in the Land! The

Fea - ture At-trac-tion Gives us Ac-tion On the Wit - ness Stand.
Fea - ture At-trac-tion Gives us Ac-tion On __ the __ Wit - ness Stand.
Fea - ture At-trac-tion Gives us Ac-tion On the Wit - ness Stand.

(Drum)

The Saga Of Jenny

128

Refrain *(leisurely)*

1. Jen-ny made her mind up when she was three, She, her-self, was going to trim the
2. Jen-ny made her mind up when she was twelve, That in-to for-eign lan-guag-es
3. Jen-ny made her mind up at twen-ty-two, To get her-self a hus-band was the
4. Jen-ny made her mind up at thir-ty-nine, She would take a trip to the
5. Jen-ny made her mind up at fif-ty-one, She would write her mem-oirs be-

p a tempo

Christ-mas tree; Christ-mas Eve she lit the can-dles, tossed the ta-pers a-way. Lit-tle
she would delve, But at sev-en-teen to Vas-sar it was quite a blow That in
thing to do, She got her-self all dolled up in her sat-ins and furs, And she
Ar-gen-tine. She was on-ly on va-ca-tion, but the Lat-ins a-gree, Jen-ny
fore she was done, The ver-y day her book was pub-lished his-t'ry re-lates There were

(small notes only for 4th refrain)   ALL

Jen-ny was an or-phan on Christ-mas day.— Poor Jen-ny!
twen-ty-sev-en lan-guag-es she could-n't say no.— Poor Jen-ny!
got her-self a hus-band, but he was-n't hers.— Poor Jen-ny!
was the one who start-ed the Good Neigh-bor pol-i-cy. Poor Jen-ny!
wives who shot their hus bands in some thir-ty-three states. Poor Jen-ny!

mf

LIZA

Bright as a pen-ny! Her e-qual would be hard to find.— She lost one dad and moth-er, A
Bright as a pen-ny! Her e-qual would be hard to find.— To Jen-ny I'm be-hold-en, Her
Bright as a pen-ny! Her e-qual would be hard to find.— De-served a bed of ros-es, But
Bright as a pen-ny! Her e-qual would be hard to find.— Oh, pas-sion does-n't van-ish, In
Bright as a pen-ny! Her e-qual would be hard to find.— She could give cards and spad-ies, To

1.-2.-3.-4.-5

sis- ter and a broth- er, But she would make up her mind.
heart was big and gold- en, But she would make up her mind.
his- to- ry dis- clos- es, That she would make up her mind.
Port- u- gese or Span- ish, But she would make up her mind.
ma- ny oth- er la- dies, But she would make up her mind.

LIZA

6. Jen- ny made her mind up at sev- en- ty- five,— She would live to be the old- est

wom- an a- live,— But gin and rum and des- ti- ny play

fun- ny tricks— And poor Jen- ny kicked the buck- et at sev- en- ty- six.—

ALL

Jen-ny points a mor-al With which you can-not quar-rel. Makes a lot of com-mon sense!____

LIZA

Jen-ny and her sa-ga Prove that you are ga-ga If you don't keep sit-ting on the fence.____

ALL

Jen-ny and her sto-ry Point the way to glo-ry To all man and wom-an kind.____

CHARLIE
A most excellent defence Miss Elliott.   May I ask what you have there?

Moderato (♩ = 88)

LIZA
Why, the circus cover.

CHARLIE
May I see it?

LIZA
Of course.

CHARLIE
Thank you.   Gentlemen, look

at this.

(He gives the circus cover to the Jury)

JURY *(humming)*

Hm ——————

LIZA
No, no. Don't! Don't! Don't sing that.

CHARLIE *(to Jury)*
You see!

CHARLIE

(to Liza) You're a-

fraid!   You're hid-ing some-thing! You're a - fraid of that mu - sic, aren't you?

Just as you're a-fraid to com-pete as a wom-an — A - fraid to mar-ry Ken-dall Nes-bitt — A-

fraid to be the wom-an you want to be! A-fraid! A-fraid! A-fraid! A-fraid!

Alla marcia (♩ = 138)

ff ALL

Ha - ha - ha - ha, Ha - ha - ha - ha, Ha - ha - ha - ha,

Ha - ha - ha - ha, Ha - ha - ha - ha, Ha - ha - ha - ha - ha.

End of 3rd Dream

IV. Childhood Dream

in. I can wait the years Till it ap-pears One fine day one spring, But the

pearls and such They won't mean much if there's miss-ing just one thing. I do not care if that

day ar - rives, That dream need nev - er be, If the ship I sing does-n't

al - so bring my own true love to me, If the ship I sing does-n't

allargando

mf più espr.

(slow)

al - so bring my own true love to me.

dim.